A NOTE TO YOUTH FROM
ONE OF YOUR AUTHORS

In the United States of America, we have freedom to choose our leaders and speak out on things we care about.

You, too, can be a leader in your school, faith community, and neighborhood. Always know that you are valuable, and you have much to offer. You can change your world for the better by reading today and becoming a brighter leader tomorrow.

Just start, and never give up!

Love and Light Always,
Portia Bright Pittman

ISBN: 978-1-7349356-0-8 (paperback)
978-1-7349356-1-5 (hardback)
978-1-7349356-2-2 (ebook)

LCCN: 2020910973

www.brightbooks.org

A BRIGHT DAY AT THE STATE CAPITOL

THERE OUGHT TO BE A LAW

Portia Bright Pittman

Dr. Calvin Mercer

Authors

Harry Aveira

Illustrator

A VISIT TO THE STATE CAPITOL

"Mom, can you take Martin and me to get ice cream?"

"Yeah, Mrs. Bright. Eliza's got a great idea. I want Cookies and Cream and Fudge Swirl!" Martin adds.

"I want chocolate!" Eliza says.

"I'm thinking about that delicious cinnamon pecan!" Mrs. Bright says. "There are a lot of different flavors of ice cream, for sure. Going for ice cream is fine, but first we're going to spend the day at the General Assembly where I work. Ice cream comes after that."

"Aww Mom! Let's eat ice cream first."

"No, Eliza. Not this time. I think you two will find our visit to the General Assembly interesting."

"What's the General Assembly, Mrs. Bright?" Martin asks.

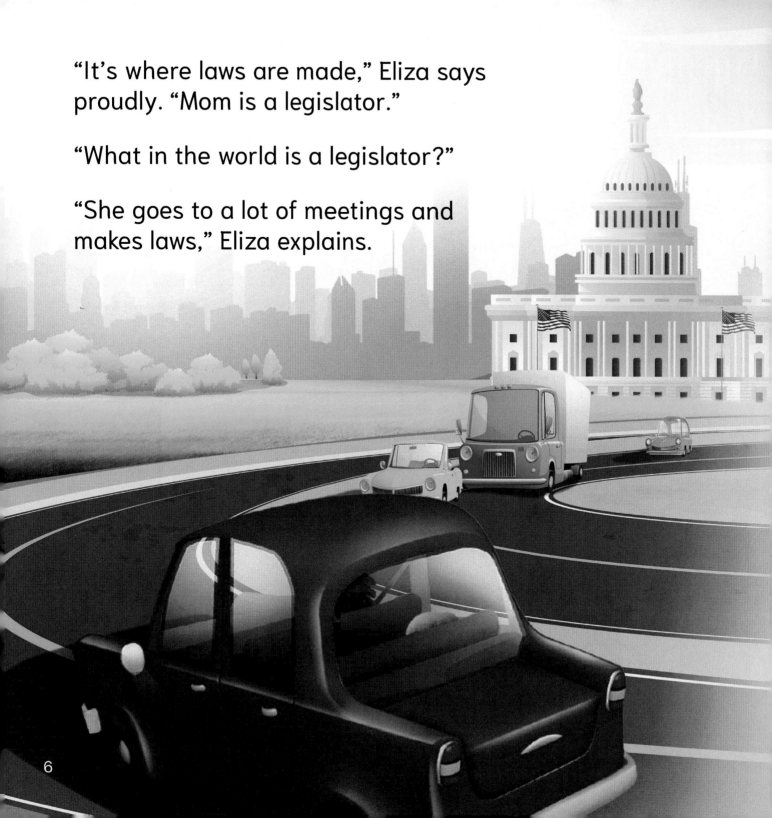

"It's where laws are made," Eliza says proudly. "Mom is a legislator."

"What in the world is a legislator?"

"She goes to a lot of meetings and makes laws," Eliza explains.

"That's right, Martin. A legislator is a lawmaker. A law is a rule, similar to the rules your parents have at your house. We'll see how laws are made in our state. If you wanted to make a law for everyone in the state, what would it be? Think about that as we drive over. Now, grab your backpacks, and let's go."

As Representative Bright, Eliza's mother, drives up to the legislative building, Eliza exclaims, "Look, Martin! That's where laws are made."

Eyes wide, Martin stares out the window at the tall, white capitol building with a golden dome and flags of the United States flying out front.

"Wow, Mrs. Bright." Martin says. "It sure is a big building."

"She's *Representative Bright*, Martin. That's her name on this trip," Eliza says proudly.

"Good morning, Representative Bright," a police officer says, greeting them just inside the big double doors. "And who are these two fine young people?"

"Officer Davis, this is my daughter, Eliza, and her friend, Martin. Martin is spending the day with us, and we're going to see how laws are made."

"And then we're going for ice cream!" Eliza tells Officer Davis.

Martin peeks past Officer Davis to the roped off, red-carpeted stairs, with gold railings winding upward.

Representative Bright, seeing Martin's excitement, says, "Those beautiful stairs lead up to a special room called the gallery. We'll go up there pretty soon, but first I want to introduce you to someone before my meeting starts."

LAW MAKING

Walking briskly down the long hallway, trailed by Eliza and Martin, Representative Bright stops at a wall of photos. She turns to Eliza and Martin, "Here are some legislators who have worked in the General Assembly making laws in years past."

"Wow!" Martin looks at photos going back more than two hundred years.

Representative Bright explains, "These are some of the highest-ranking members of the General Assembly, such as the President Pro Tempore of the Senate and Speaker of the House of Representatives."

"But mom," Eliza says, looking confused, "I don't see many people who look like us in the pictures. "

"Yeah," Martin says, "but people of color can make laws, too."

Representative Bright adds, "That's a very good observation, Martin. Many people have worked hard and suffered so people of all races can have the opportunity to be lawmakers. If they hadn't stood up for what they believed, I wouldn't be a legislator today."

"OK, guys, let's keep going. We've got laws to make."

Representative Bright stops at her office where she's greeted by a young man in coat and tie. "Hello, Representative Bright," he says, then turning to Eliza. "And you must be Eliza."

"How did you know my name?" Eliza asks.

"Your mom talks about you all the time. I'm your mom's Legislative Assistant. My name is Benjamin."

"Oh," Eliza says, her face shining. "Sure wish I had an assistant! I need some help cleaning my room."

Representative Bright chuckles. "This is Martin, Eliza's best friend. Martin lives across the street from Eliza, and they've been best friends since kindergarten when they tied for first place in the class sack race. Martin is spending the day with Eliza. The two of them have been thinking about a law they'd like to get passed."

"Great," Benjamin says, "We'll learn how to pass a law. It'll be fun. But, first, we've got to get Eliza's mom to her important committee meeting."

Representative Bright grabs papers from her office desk. "Alright, you two, let's go. The meeting starts in five minutes."

Out the door they go.

Benjamin, Eliza, and Martin sit at the back of the meeting room, listening to legislators talk about making laws.

Crack! Crack! Crack! Eliza and Martin jump when they hear a sound like a bat hitting a baseball, then a loud voice, "Meeting adjourned!"

"That's the chairperson ending the meeting," Benjamin explains. "Now, let's head to the gallery."

"Chairperson? Why is somebody in charge of the chairs?" Martin asks.

Chuckling, Benjamin explains that a chairperson is in charge of a meeting.

Representative Bright leads everyone to the winding stairs. She leaves them, and they climb the many stairs to the gallery.

"What's the gallery?" Eliza asks, as she and Martin grab seats at the front, staring down into a huge room where legislators are gathering.

"The gallery is where guests like us can watch laws being made. Look down there," Benjamin says, pointing.

"There's your mom," Martin says.

Crack! Crack! Crack! "The meeting will now come to order," a voice bellows from the front of the large room below them. "We are in session. Please stand for our opening."

Eliza and Martin, along with the other guests, dutifully stand with their hands over their hearts for the Pledge of Allegiance.

"Let us pray," an elderly man begins. "Please bless these honorable legislators as they make laws that protect our people and bring prosperity to our land. Thank you for your guidance in these proceedings. Amen."

Eliza turns to Benjamin, "That was short. In our church we pray long prayers."

Benjamin, with a smile on his face, explains, "This is the state government. It's not a church. A lot of different religions are represented here. This prayer is general enough to include everyone's faith."

"You mean like that woman," Eliza says, pointing to the far side of the room.

"Yes, she's wearing a hijab," Benjamin says.

"Is something wrong with her head?" Martin says.

"No," Eliza says. "A hi–jab. It's a scarf that some women in the Muslim religion wear."

"Oh yeah," Martin says. "I saw a girl wearing one at school. I thought she was just cold. One boy made fun of the girl, and she started to cry."

Benjamin frowns. "I'm sorry to hear that. There's a lot of bullying in schools."

He continues, "You may not cover your head in your church, but Muslim women do. And religious Jewish men wear a small head covering called a kippah."

"People are different, just like different flavors of ice cream," Eliza says.

Benjamin nods, "Your mom and other legislators make laws for everyone in our state, no matter what religion or race they are."

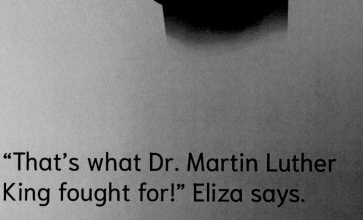

"That's what Dr. Martin Luther King fought for!" Eliza says.

"That's right, Eliza. He wanted everyone to be treated fairly. Look below, and you'll see different races, as well as men and women. It's like mixing different flavors of ice cream to make one milkshake."

24

"Look!" Martin exclaims. A youth was walking quickly across the floor below. "That's a kid. What's he doing down there? Is he a representative?"

"Good eye Martin," Benjamin says. "That's a page. A page is a high school student who runs important errands for the representatives. See, he's taking a note to one of the legislators."

"Wow, that looks like a cool job," Eliza says.

"It's a lot of fun. If you make good grades and participate in your school, in a few years you can apply to be a page and help make laws."

"When can we learn how to make our law?" Eliza asks.

"Well, while your mom and other legislators are making their laws, let's take a trip to the snack shop, and I'll explain all the steps in making laws."

REPRESENTATIVES FOR A DAY

As they take seats at a table with soda and corn chips, Benjamin surprises them. "How would you two like to be representatives like Eliza's mom?"

"That's not possible," Eliza says. "Mom had to work hard on her campaign and get lots of votes to be a representative. Who's going to elect us? We're just kids!"

Benjamin smiles. "I am. I elect you, Eliza and Martin, to be representatives for a day. This means you can pass any law you want, and I'm going to tell you how to do it. How's that?"

"Awesome," Eliza says. "Will my brother have to do what I say?"

"I don't know about that!" Benjamin says, smiling. "So, what law do you want to pass?"

Martin has an idea. "How about we make a law that kids get free ice cream whenever they want?"

"Yeah!" Eliza says. "There ought to be a law! And I've been thinking about the kids at school being bullied. How about a bullying law, too?"

"I've been bullied," Martin says. "It's no fun. There ought to be a law about that too."

Benjamin smiles, "You can do one law that includes both bullying and ice cream."

Eliza says, "I can vote for that!"

"OK, you need to know some things before your idea becomes a law."

"I'm ready," Eliza says, with a big grin. "You ready, Representative Martin?"

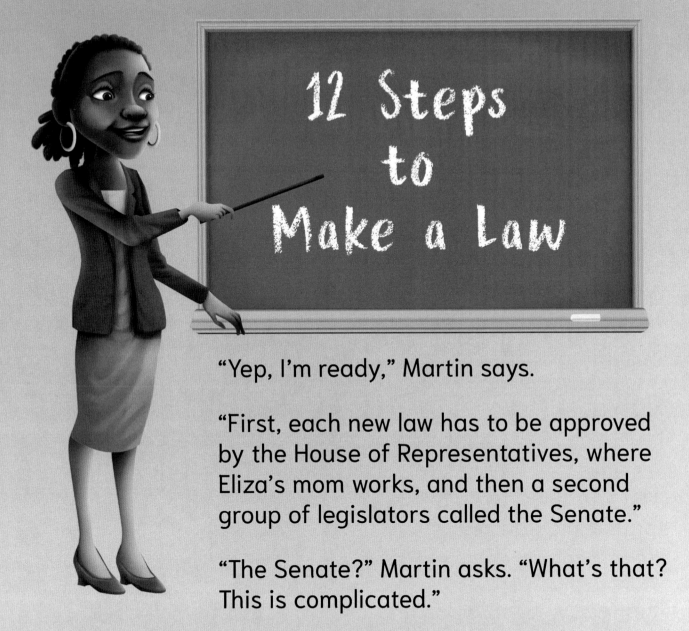

12 Steps to Make a Law

"Yep, I'm ready," Martin says.

"First, each new law has to be approved by the House of Representatives, where Eliza's mom works, and then a second group of legislators called the Senate."

"The Senate?" Martin asks. "What's that? This is complicated."

"It can be," Benjamin says. "But you want to make a law, right? We have to understand how it all works. The House of Representatives and Senate make up the General Assembly that makes laws. This is important work, because people in your school and neighborhood have to follow the laws."

"I'm ready. Let's make our law," Eliza says.

"You two representatives have an idea about preventing bullying and providing free ice cream. Your idea has to go through 12 steps before it becomes a law. You can have an anti-bullying law and then add your idea about free ice cream as an amendment."

"An amendment? What's that?" Eliza says.

"An amendment is an addition to a law. Anti-bullying would be the main law, and you'd add an addition to it called a free ice cream amendment."

"What do we want our anti-bullying law to say?" Eliza asks.

"I know!" Martin says. "If you pick on somebody, then you can't go out for recess for two whole months."

"And if you do it again, you can't go on any field trips," Eliza adds.

Benjamin nods, "That's pretty good. Let's think about a name for your law."

Martin has an idea. "I know. We can call it the 'Don't Stomp on Me' law. Everybody has to obey it."

THE 12 STEPS TO PASS A LAW

"That's a good name," Benjamin says. "I like it. Now, let's take your idea through the 12 steps. There's no guarantee it will make it through all 12 steps, but it's worth a try, right?"

Eliza and Martin nod in agreement.

"The first step is getting your idea written into a bill," Benjamin explains.

"A bill?" Martin says. "Do you mean write it on a dollar bill?"

"No, Martin. When you write your idea down, it becomes a bill, and that's **STEP 1**. Listen carefully because you can't skip any of the steps, or your idea won't become a law."

"After writing it down, in **STEP 2** you give it to the Principal of Clerks Office where it's given a number. Getting a number is **STEP 3**. Not too hard so far, right?"

Benjamin can tell that making a law is harder than they thought.

"**STEP 4** is a fun step. Your 'Don't Stomp on Me' bill is read on the floor of the House. That means someone reads it out loud in the House of Representatives which we saw when we were sitting in the gallery."

"Oh boy," Eliza says, showing new interest. "I like that room."

Don't Stomp On Me

Bullying is wrong

"Well, good," Benjamin continues. "You'll also want to speak with your friends in the legislature to get them to agree with your idea. It's like when you get your friends to try your favorite ice cream flavor."

"We can do that," Eliza says. "We have friends who don't like bullying. What do we do next?"

FREE
ICE
CREAM

"One of your friends can offer the addition to your bill, the amendment, that kids can get free ice cream whenever they want it."

"Yeah," Martin says, nodding his head enthusiastically. "A lot of our friends will like the ice cream amendment."

"OK," Benjamin says. "Your law is moving right along. Next, the bill goes to a committee, like the meeting we sat in with Eliza's mom this morning. The committee gives its opinion about the bill, and that's **STEP 5**."

"Who wouldn't like this bill?" Eliza asks, with a puzzled look.

"Yes, we hope the bill is very popular," Benjamin says. "In **STEPS 6 AND 7**, the bill is read two more times in the House of Representatives where Eliza's mom works."

Don't Stomp On Me

"It sure takes a lot to get this done," Martin says. "Why do they read the bill again and again?"

Benjamin says, "They read it several times, because all the people in our state have to obey these laws. It's important to get the bill right and give the legislators plenty of time to discuss it and add amendments."

"In **STEP 8**, they make sure most of the legislators agree with the ice cream amendment. Then the Senate approves your bill, which is **STEP 9**."

"Oh, I forgot about the Senate," Eliza says. "I hope they like ice cream and don't like bullying."

SENATE

"We almost have a new law. Once the House and Senate votes for your bill, it is sent to the state governor in **STEP 10**. If the governor likes your bill, he or she signs it, and that's **STEP 11**."

Don't Stomp on Me

GOVERNOR

"What's a governor?" Martin asks.

"The governor is sort of like the president," Eliza explains. "Except that the governor helps lead a state."

"Is the governor like the principal of our school?" Martin asks.

"Yes, but the state is much bigger than our school," Eliza says.

"I sure hope the governor likes ice cream," Martin says.

"Mom knows the governor, so Mom can help us," Eliza says.

Benjamin smiles. "Finally, in **STEP 12**, the law is given a number. That's how your 'Don't Stomp on Me' bill, with a free ice cream amendment, could become a law."

41

"Hey, there's mom!" Eliza exclaims, as Representative Bright darts into the snack shop.

"You're just in time, Representative Bright, it's been a bright day at the state capitol," Benjamin says, smiling.

"We just learned how a bill gets passed into a law," Martin says.

"Sounds like you have been busy. I'm all ears," she says, taking a chair at the table with them.

"Mom, we're passing a law against bullying," Eliza says.

Martin adds, "It's the 'Don't Stomp on Me' law, and we're going to add an amendment that gives free ice cream to any kid that wants it."

"Now, you two legislators, I want to hear all about it. How about you tell me what you learned while we drive to the ice cream shop?"

44

Eliza and Martin jump off their seats and grab their backpacks.

"I'm ready for ice cream, Mom," Eliza says.

"Cookies and Cream and Fudge Swirl!" Martin excitedly agrees.

"Cookies and Cream and Fudge Swirl and Chocolate and Vanilla for me. I want a lot of different flavors!" Eliza adds.

"I can't wait for our next adventure," Martin says.

The End.

STOP

NO BULLIES
BEYOND
THIS POINT

YOUR AUTHORS

Portia Bright Pittman

Portia served as legislative assistant for lawmakers in the North Carolina Senate and House of Representatives.

She earned her start in politics by successfully managing a North Carolina House campaign for Representative Jean Farmer-Butterfield and a city council campaign for her coauthor. She expresses her passion for youth by helping them understand how government works.

Portia leads programs for schools, faith communities, and civic groups about the legislative process. Contact her at brightbooks@brightbooks.org for details.

Calvin Mercer, PhD

Professor of Religion at East Carolina University, Dr. Mercer has written widely about the Bible and other topics in religion.

His passion is helping faith communities and other groups understand how artificial intelligence, robotics, genetic engineering, and other breakthrough technologies are going to radically change our bodies, emotions, and minds.

Dr. Mercer served a decade on the Greenville, NC, City Council and works to engage citizens in their government.

He speaks widely on subjects of his books and volunteers in his wife's church youth group. Contact him at mercerc@ecu.edu.

WORDS IN YOUR BOOK

To be helpful, words that are in **bold** and **underlined** are in the list, in case you need to look them up.

AMENDMENT: An addition to a **bill** that could become a **law**. Eliza and Martin learn to create an anti-bullying **law** with an **amendment** of free ice cream for kids.

BILL: A potential **law** is called a **bill** while **legislators** are taking it through the 12 steps.

CAMPAIGN: The hard work of many people to get people to **vote** a certain way. Eliza's mom had campaigned to be a **representative**.

CAPITOL: The building where **legislators** meet to make **laws**. That's where **Representative** Bright works.

CHAIRPERSON: The **chairperson** is in charge of a **committee** that comes up with ideas for **laws**. The **chairperson** is the one who bangs the **gavel** on the table to get the attention of people on the **committee**.

COMMITTEE: A group of people who, in your book, come up with ideas for **laws**.

GALLERY: The room where Eliza, Martin, and other visitors to the **capitol** sit to watch **Representative** Bright and other **legislators** work to make **laws**.

GAVEL: A small wooden hammer that the **chairperson** of a **committee** bangs on the table to get everyone's attention.

GENERAL ASSEMBLY: The big group of all the **legislators** who make **laws** for your **state**.

GOVERNOR: The head of a **state**. The **governor** is like the president of the United States, except that **states** are much smaller.

HOUSE OF REPRESENTATIVES: The **House of Representatives** is one of two groups of **legislators** that make up the **General Assembly**.

LAW: A **rule**. It takes a long time and a lot of work when **legislators** make **rules** for your **state**.

LEGISLATION: Another word for **laws** that are made by **legislators** like **Representative** Bright.

LEGISLATIVE ASSISTANT: A hard-working person who helps **representatives** make good **laws** for your **state**.

LEGISLATOR: A person who makes **laws** in your **state**.

MARTIN LUTHER KING, JR.: A hero who fought hard so that **laws** would be fair and protect everyone.

PAGE: A high school student who works in the **state Capitol**, helping **legislators** make good **laws** for your **state**. When they looked down into the **gallery**, Eliza and Martin saw a **page** running errands for **legislators**.

PRESIDENT PRO TEMPORE: The **President Pro Tempore**, also called "President Pro-Tem," is the leader of the **Senate**. This person leads the meetings and has a lot of power and influence in what **laws** are made.

PRINCIPAL OF CLERKS OFFICE: This is where **bills** that might become **laws** are given an official number, so they can be **voted** on by **legislators**.

SENATE: The **Senate** is one of two groups of **legislators** that make up the **General Assembly**, the big group that makes **laws** for your **state**.

SPEAKER OF THE HOUSE: The **Speaker** is the leader of the House of **Representatives**. This person leads the meetings and has a lot of power and influence in what **laws** are made.

STATE: In the United States of America, sometimes called the "USA," there are 50 **states**.

VOTE: To pick something. **Legislators** vote for some **bills** to become **laws**. Also, a lot of people voted for Eliza's mom to be a **representative**.

ONE BIG FUN SENTENCE

In your **state Capitol**, after a lot of work in **committees** and with the help of **legislative assistants**, **bills** become **laws**—which are **rules**—with **amendments**, when **legislators** in the **House of Representatives** and **Senate**, making up the **General Assembly**, meet in the **gallery** and vote.

Can you make up other sentences using words from the vocabulary?

ENDORSEMENTS

"I loved the book! I wish I'd had access to this book back in the day when I was teaching fourth grade social studies and needed a more realistic way to explain laws and legislative processes. The day ends in a long-awaited trip to get ice cream, and the reader can almost taste the deliciousness of the treat along with the fun of learning. The mixture of messages against bullying makes for some subtle learning about the negative effects of bullying for children."

Dr. Patricia Anderson, Professor of Elementary Education, East Carolina University

"The illustrations bring the characters to life. This book addresses stereotypes and is inclusive of different races, ethnic backgrounds, religions, and gender. It is an outstanding instructional resource for teaching state government and provides an opportunity for students to brainstorm current issues that could be passed as a law while focusing on essential government vocabulary! Well done! I am excited about seeing this book in our classrooms!"

Beth Uffers, NBCT, County Teacher of the Year

"This engaging, informative book simplifies the 12-step law-making process so that children (and adults) may understand clearly the terminology and complexities involved in the formulation of state laws. Both Social Studies teachers and homeschool parents will find this text useful, but they should be prepared to serve ice cream after sharing with their students!"

Dalene Parker, Ed.D, NBCT

THANK YOU!

Sign up to hear about free downloads, new products, specials, events, and more. You can also schedule us for a school visit or sponsor your school with copies of the book.

Visit our website at
www.brightbooks.org

Made in United States
Orlando, FL
19 February 2024